John

D0919337

DANIEL BOONE

Boy Hunter

BY

Augusta Stevenson

ILLUSTRATED BY
Paul Laune

THE BOBBS-MERRILL COMPANY

Publishers

INDIANAPOLIS   NEW YORK

DEDICATED

TO ALL THOSE YOUNG FOLLOWERS OF

DANIEL BOONE'S WOODCRAFT, THE

BOY SCOUTS OF AMERICA

CONTENTS

LIST OF FULL-PAGE ILLUSTRATIONS

DANIEL BOONE

Boy Hunter

I

BEARS AND BEES AND HONEY TREES

"My goodness!" cried young Daniel Boone. "My goodness, Mr. McGuire! Didn't you have but one bullet left when you saw that bear?"

"That's all, Dannie," said the great hunter. "You see, I'd been hunting all day and I was bound for my camp when it happened."

Daniel sat on a three-legged stool by the fireplace facing the visitor. Now the other Boones drew their chairs and stools closer. Mr. McGuire always told a good story every time he came. They didn't want to miss a word.

"I've been in all kinds of trouble out in the woods," said Pete McGuire. "But I was never in more danger, never in all my life.

"I guess the bear and I smelled the honey at

13

about the same time. We probably started for the honey tree at about the same time, too. And I think we both decided to get that honey the minute we smelled it. I know I did."

"Of course," said the Boones.

"The scent came from the south," Pete continued, "so south I went. Before long I saw the bees. They were flying in and out of an old oak tree.

"I made my way there as fast as I could. There was thick brush to go through and that slowed me up some."

The older Boone boys nodded. Israel, Samuel and Jonathan knew all about thick brush slowing up anyone. Even Daniel knew that and he was only eight years old.

"Suddenly I heard a queer sort of noise," Pete went on. "It wasn't far away, either. It was something moving through the brush and it was big and heavy."

"How could you tell that?" asked Samuel.

"Why, by the crackling of the branches and the thud of padded feet. I thought it was a bear so I 'froze' in my tracks and waited."

Again the Boone boys nodded. They had had

Mr. McGuire always told a good story every time he came.

to "freeze" many a time themselves. They knew it took courage to stand perfectly still while the danger came closer and closer. One move and the enemy would know your hiding place. But Pete McGuire wouldn't move. Not he! He was the best hunter in the Pennsylvania wilderness.

Now he was talking again. "It wasn't long until I saw the creature. It was a bear, a cinnamon bear. He hadn't scented me yet: the wind was wrong—for him.

"But he had scented the honey. I could tell that by the way he'd stop every now and then and sniff the air."

"Bears like honey, don't they?" said young Elizabeth.

"They love it," said Pete. "They'll do anything to get it. They even kill each other fighting for it."

"They even kill themselves," said Mr. Squire Boone, Daniel's father. "They'll climb out on limbs that can't hold them. Then they fall and break their necks or backs."

"I know that's true," said Pete. "I've found their skeletons under honey trees. Every one had a broken neck or back."

"That seems a pity," said Sarah Boone, Daniel's gentle Quaker mother.

"Well, they had to have their honey," said Squire.

"What happened next?" asked Daniel.

"The wind changed all of a sudden and blew from me to the cinnamon. He got my scent and then he saw me. For one instant he looked straight at me. And, folks, I know you won't believe it, but that bear passed right on by!"

"Ha, ha!" laughed the Boones. They didn't believe it.

"It's a fact," said Pete. "He knew I was after the honey and he was afraid I'd get there first. At least, that's what I thought he thought. But I was thinking, too, and I meant to beat him to the oak."

"Why didn't you shoot him and make sure?" asked Jonathan, who was more often called John.

"Have you forgotten that I had just one bullet?" Pete asked.

"Well, you wouldn't have missed him. Father says you never miss."

"I was afraid to risk a shot. I might just wound him. Then he'd attack me and I might never eat honey again. So I ran for the oak and I didn't run any too soon. That bear had the same idea. He made a dash for the old oak, too. It was a race between us. And I barely made it. I felt his breath on my feet as I started to climb."

"Weren't you scared?" asked Sally.

"I was, and I was still more scared when he climbed right after me."

"I don't blame you," said Squire. "I wouldn't want to be in the same tree with a cinnamon."

"His breath made it bad for me, too. It spread out all through the tree just like steam. I couldn't see the bees. I could hardly see the branches I was climbing."

"Is thee not stretching the truth a little?" asked Mrs. Boone.

"Well, maybe I am, Sarah—a little."

"Now, Sarah," said her husband, "Pete has to put in a joke or two. The children understand that."

"Of course!" cried the children.

"Then thee may go on with thy stretching, Pete," said Sarah with a smile.

Mr. McGuire smiled back. He knew how Quakers felt about telling the truth. It had to be the exact truth.

"Go on!" cried Daniel. "What happened next?"

"Well, sir, that bear began to act mighty strange. He stopped climbing and began to paw at the tree. He tore off strips of bark and threw them down. And all the time he was growling so loud it sounded like thunder."

Pete looked at Sarah. "Maybe not quite so loud," he said quickly, "but mighty near it."

Mrs. Boone nodded and smiled. Then Pete continued. "Never saw a bear so mad. Guess he thought I'd get to the honey first and he was talking out loud about it."

"Ha, ha!" laughed the Boones.

"However, he didn't keep that up very long. He began to climb again. I climbed higher. He climbed higher. And don't you forget this, folks —cinnamons can certainly climb."

The Boones nodded. They wouldn't forget. They knew it anyway.

"Well, just then I had a little good luck. A strong breeze blew away his breath and I could see the bees. They were flying into a hollow limb just above me."

"Was the honey there?" asked Elizabeth.

"Yes, my dear. And if that big limb was only half full there would be a thousand pounds or so."

"Of course," nodded the Boones.

"I was close enough now to help myself. I wouldn't mind a few stings. But would I have time? The bear was almost within reach of me."

"Oh my goodness!" cried Daniel.

"I thought I'd just grab a handful of honey and jump. In fact I looked down to see how far it was to the ground. And what do you think I saw?"

"A deep ravine," said Sam.

"A precipice," said John.

"No. *I saw another bear!*"

"Oh!" cried the boys.

"Oh my!" cried the girls.

"I knew this bear had scented the honey, for she was sniffing the air. So I knew she'd be climbing the oak in a minute or so."

"Of course!" cried all the Boones.

"Just then I heard a loud buzzing just above me. I looked up and if I didn't see a million wild honey bees coming out of that limb!"

"My! My!" said Mrs. Boone. "A million!"

"Well, ten thousand or so," said Pete.

The Boones smiled and Mr. McGuire continued. "I knew what had happened. The bear's hot breath had driven them out."

"Of course," said the Boones.

"Then I didn't know what to do. If I went up, the bees would sting me to death. If I climbed down, I'd be hugged to death. If I jumped down, I'd be clawed to death.

"So there I was. I couldn't go up. I couldn't go down. I couldn't jump and I couldn't run. What was I to do?"

The Boones shook their heads. They didn't know how anyone could get out of such a fix.

"What did you do?" asked Mr. Boone.

"Well, sir, I didn't do anything. The bees saved me. They swarmed."

"Swarmed!" cried the Boones.

Pete nodded. "The old queen had left the hive

The bear tried to get rid of them . . . but the bees stuck tight.

and part of the others were following her. They were looking for a new home, Dannie."

"I know how they do," said Daniel.

"They found one, too, right away. And you'll never guess where it was."

"Where?" asked the Boones.

"On the cinnamon's nose!"

"Ha, ha!" laughed the others.

"He tried to get rid of them. He pawed at his nose. He rubbed it against the tree but the bees stuck tight.

"Then he climbed down and tried again to get rid of his new friends. He jumped up and down. He rolled over and over and stood on his head. But the swarm didn't leave. I really felt sorry for him.

"Help was near, however. The other bear began to talk to him. She was coaxing him to do something. I could tell that by her soft little whines. Suddenly she went to the creek and he followed.

"She jumped in. He jumped in. She put her head under the water. He put his head under the water. You know what happened then."

"Of course!" laughed the Boones.

"That's right," nodded Pete. "The swarm left the minute his head touched water."

"Well, well!" exclaimed Squire. "That's a good story, Pete. It makes me feel homesick for another hunt with you."

"Didn't you get any honey, Mr. McGuire?" asked Daniel.

"Indeed I did, Dannie. I filled my coonskin cap with it. Then I climbed down and ran. And just as soon as I was safe in my camp I ate every bit of it. I didn't want a crowd of bears coming to see me that night."

"Was that the only reason thee ate it all right away?" asked Mrs. Boone.

Mr. McGuire smiled. "Well, Sarah, I always did like honey pretty well."

"I'm going to find a honey tree when I'm a hunter," said Daniel.

"Find yourself a couple of cinnamons, too," said Israel.

"I will," said Daniel gravely.

Everyone laughed and soon after they all went to bed and dreamed of bears and bees and honey trees.

II

LIFE IN THE WILDERNESS

1. Farming, Weaving, Teaching

MR. McGUIRE had gone and the Boones were busy with their fall work. The older boys were gathering corn. They took care of their father's farm now, for they were almost young men. Israel was sixteen. Sam was fourteen and John was twelve.

The farm was on the edge of the Pennsylvania wilderness in the little settlement of Exeter. But there was no other cabin within a mile, nor any other farm or clearing.

These boys saw nothing as they worked but the endless forest. It surrounded their clearing. It towered above their cabin and barn. It shut them in like an army of soldiers.

But they didn't mind that. It would take more

than a dark forest to frighten those strong frontier boys.

Up to this year their father had managed the farm. Now he spent all his time weaving. He wove cloth for almost everyone in Exeter and also for his own family. He even had orders from the city of Philadelphia, many miles away.

There was no better weaver anywhere than Squire Boone. He had four looms in a little weaving-house just back of the cabin. Three of them were always in use.

The oldest daughter, Sally, had learned to weave from her father and worked with him. Bessie (Elizabeth) was learning now. Mrs. Boone also helped whenever she had time.

"I should help thee today, Squire," she said one morning. "Thee has more than thee can do. But I must help Daniel with his spelling. I told him I would and I must keep my word."

"Of course thee must, Sarah. Thee always keeps thy word."

"Ah, it sounds good to hear thee use our Quaker language, Squire. Thee does not use it often."

"I know, I seem to forget to use it. I talk with so many who are not Quakers."

Sarah sighed. "It is the same way with the children. They also are forgetting to use our language. But it can't be helped. So many new settlers are coming and so few of them are Quakers. I shall be thankful if I remember it myself."

"Oh, thee will never forget. Thee is too good a Quaker for that."

Sarah smiled; then she became serious. "I would like Daniel to use our language. He is so bright and quick. He would make a splendid Quaker preacher."

"Well, I don't know about that, Sarah. Seems to me he'd rather kill bears."

"I don't want him to be a hunter, Squire. I'll keep him from it if I can."

"Maybe thy teaching will change him."

"Oh, I hope so!" said Sarah. "I hope so!"

2. "Then Something Did Happen!"

"Squire," said Sarah a few weeks later, "I must talk with thee about Daniel. He is not doing well with his lessons. He gets out of them every time he can. I never can find him when I am ready. I fear he hides away."

"I know he does. I've caught him at it several times and sent him in to you."

"He should have a real teacher. It's too bad we haven't a school in the settlement."

"It is too bad. But no teacher will come this far away from Philadelphia."

"There goes Daniel now!" cried Sarah. "He's running toward the garden."

"Daniel!" she called.

But Daniel didn't seem to hear. He kept right on running.

"D-A-N-I-E-L!" called Mr. Boone.

That time Daniel heard. His father's voice hinted of a hickory switch in the barn. He came back in a hurry.

"Did thee not know it was time for lessons?" asked his mother.

"Oh, I thought I'd better dig some potatoes for dinner. I was afraid it might rain."

"It will not rain," said his father.

"And I have plenty of potatoes," said his mother.

"Walk straight into the cabin, young man, and get to work on your spelling," said Mr. Boone.

"Yes, sir," said Daniel meekly. He followed his mother inside and watched her get the speller from the mantel shelf.

"I wish something would happen," he said to

himself. "I wouldn't care what it was—an earthquake or anything."

Then something did happen! Bessie ran into the cabin as white as a sheet. She was so frightened she could hardly speak.

"Indians!" she gasped. "Strange Indians! They came out of the forest! They're coming this way!"

Mrs. Boone ran to the door and bolted it. Then she seized her rifle and looked through the peephole.

An old trail passed through the Boone clearing and by the cabin door. Sarah could see the Indians plainly.

She saw at once they were not Delawares, the friendly tribe that lived all about them. These strange Indians were painted differently. Their feathers were different. Their moccasins seemed different, too, but she wasn't sure. They were walking so fast she couldn't see the bead pattern.

"Strange Indians! They're coming this way!"

33

Suddenly the last one stopped. A snake was crossing the path. Now Sarah had a good look at his moccasins. She knew that bead pattern! She knew the tribe. She knew where they lived.

She noticed another thing, too. They didn't even glance at the cabin. They passed by holding their heads high and scowling fiercely.

Presently she turned and put her rifle back in a corner. "They've gone on," she said. "There's nothing to be feared from them this time. And thee was right, Bessie. They were different from our Indians around here. They belong to that fierce tribe over the mountains."

"Their faces were different, too," said Bessie.

"They were scowling. They don't like white people and they want us to know it. They've never been friendly like our Delaware tribe. They seldom come to the settlement. Always hide from them, children."

"I know how to hide from Indians," said Bessie.

"Thee should. Thee is ten years old and thee has been taught. But thee has never had lessons, Daniel. Thee shall have one today."

Daniel jumped up from his stool. "I'll get Israel to teach me right away!"

"Sit down," said Mrs. Boone firmly. "Israel can teach thee later on. Thee cannot get out of thy spelling lesson."

III

DANIEL'S SAFETY LESSONS
1. He Learns to Hide

Daniel's older brothers were teaching him to hide. They took turns at this but they didn't take turns being strict. Each one was strict all the time.

If Daniel made the least noise when he hid in a thicket he had to try again. If a leaf rustled when he hid in brush he had to try again.

He had to practice hiding behind trees, rocks, logs, stumps and vines. And not a twig could be broken or a stone overturned. There must be no sign anywhere of his hiding place.

It was hard to do, all of it. The hardest of all was to hide behind vines and not leave them swinging.

"I'll never learn to do that," he said.

"You must," Israel answered. "Suppose a savage was after you and the only place you could hide was behind vines. How long do you think it would take him to find you if they were moving?"

"He might think it was the wind."

"He'd look to be sure. Indians are smart. You can't count on them forgetting anything."

"I'll practice," said Daniel.

He had a hard time also with footprints. He left some every time.

One day he was delighted. "Look, Israel!" he cried. "I didn't leave any prints this time. I mean, no one would notice them, they're so light."

"Light!" cried his brother. "They'd scream aloud to an Indian."

"I don't see why I have to be so careful. There's no Indians after me. We're at peace with them."

"We are today, but no one knows what will happen tomorrow. We all have to be ready."

"I'll practice," said Daniel.

For weeks and weeks the boy practiced. Slowly he became quicker and lighter on his feet. He left fewer and fewer signs.

Then he began the game of finding others who hid from him—his father, brothers and sisters.

It wasn't a nice little game of "I Spy," either. The hiders had to be traced by signs they had left. It might be a broken twig, crushed moss, bent grass, an overturned stone, swinging vines or footprints.

His father could disappear while Daniel was looking at him. He seemed to fade away into the forest, leaving not a trace or sign. Daniel could never find him.

Sometimes he found his brothers and sisters but not often.

"You can't expect to learn all this in a month or so," said Mr. Boone. "It may take a year or two."

2. Direction Lessons

Squire Boone, like all other settlers in Exeter, let his cows graze in the woods all winter. And the Boone boys, like all the settlers' boys, had to bring these cows home to be milked. It was John's work now.

The Boone boys, like all settlers' boys, had to bring the cows home to be milked.

It wasn't hard to find the cows, for they wore bells around their necks. But it was hard to find the way out of the forest. There was great danger of getting lost.

So every boy in Exeter had to learn directions. And he couldn't go after the cows until he knew them—north, south, east and west. He had to be able to find them in a gloomy forest. There would be no one to show him. And if he should get lost, he might never see his home again, unless a searching party found him.

Every boy was proud of himself when he was allowed to go into the woods alone. That meant he had graduated from the School of Directions.

Daniel Boone was exactly like these other boys. He could hardly wait for the time to come when he could go alone and listen for those tinkling bells. So he was delighted when Israel gave him his first Directions Lesson.

"If you learn how to find the north, you'll

never get lost," said Israel. "At night, the North Star will show you. There are several ways to find it in the daytime."

"I know one: the moss at the base of trees. It will be thinner on the north side and not so green."

"That's one way," said his brother. Then he blindfolded Daniel and led him along a cow path. Presently he stopped, turned the boy around three times and then took off the blindfold.

"Now then," he said, "point to the north."

Daniel looked for moss but there wasn't any, not on any tree in sight.

"I don't know," he said. "Which way is it?"

"You must find that out for yourself."

"Do you think I'd better go on till I find moss?"

"What would you do if you were alone?"

"I guess I'd walk on and look."

"Very well, I'll follow."

Daniel walked and walked and looked and looked, but he didn't see any moss.

"I don't understand it," he said at last. "I thought there was always moss on the north side of trees."

"Not unless there is dampness. This part of the forest is close to the clearing. So the sun has had a chance to dry things out. You'll have to look for other signs."

Daniel looked and looked, round about and up and down. Then he shook his head. "I don't see any signs."

"What about the sun? Doesn't that tell you?"

"Oh! I do see spots of sunlight on those beeches."

"Where is the sun in the late afternoon?"

"In the west. Of course! I have it now! That way where the sun spots are, is west. Then that way would be north."

"That's right, Dan. Now you're beginning to think things out."

Later on, Daniel learned to tell directions by the growth of vines and the bark of trees. Both were thicker on the sunny south side.

But still he wasn't allowed to go to the woods alone. "You must study tracks first," said his father.

3. Tracking, Listening, Calling

Now began some very hard lessons on Tracking. His brothers were his teachers and they were just as strict as they were about the Hiding Lessons.

They made the tracks of the fierce animals in the barnyard with pointed sticks. Daniel studied them as carefully as if it were arithmetic. It took hours and days and weeks before he knew them.

Then his lessons became harder. Instead of a

bear's tracks, he had to learn the tracks of a bear and her cubs.

Instead of the tracks of a wildcat, he had to learn the tracks of a wildcat and her kittens.

Or he might have to study the prints of a doe and her fawn. Or two stags and a doe. Or a stag, a doe and a fawn. Sometimes it was like working out a puzzle.

The snows had come and gone before he learned them. And spring had come and gone before he learned the tracks of small animals —raccoons, woodchucks, weasels, chipmunks, squirrels and many others.

To make it still harder he was taking two other studies at the same time: Listening and Calling.

He had to listen to the calls and cries of birds and beasts. Then he had to learn to make them.

It didn't take him long to hoot like an owl, coo like a turtle dove, howl like a wolf and cry like a panther. He'd been practicing these ever since he was six years old.

Then one day Mr. Boone told Daniel he could go after the cows. "You've done very well," he said. "I'm pleased with the way you have studied."

"He hasn't done so well with his reading and spelling," said Mrs. Boone. "He hardly ever has time for a lesson."

"These other studies were necessary," said Mr. Boone. "Now we know he'll come out of the forest alive."

IV

FUN IN THE WOODS

1. What Daniel Saw in the Shadows

AT FIRST Daniel was glad when the cowbells rang close to the clearing. And at first he hurried toward them. He hurried the cows homeward, too. The woods was gloomy in the late afternoon. There was no telling what was in those dark shadows.

After a time his eyes became so keen he could see right through the shadows. Then he was astonished: there was so much going on.

"Why," he said to himself, "it's just like a crowd of people having a good time. It's like the Fair." So every day he sat on a log quietly and watched.

He saw field mice playing a game, a meadow

lark dancing, a striped chipmunk watching and cottontails leaping over the ground.

It was different every day. Sometimes there was no playing. Every little creature seemed to have business somewhere.

Daniel was glad there were no fierce animals about to pounce on them. His father had told him that panthers, bears, wildcats and wolves were seldom found near clearings. They didn't like men and farms and had gone far away, deeper into the forest.

So he watched in safety, and always he saw wonderful things happen. He had something to tell every evening.

At first his brothers laughed. "Oh, you just imagine those things," they said.

But his mother didn't laugh. "Never thee mind, Dan'l," she said. "I am glad thee can see things in the woods that no one else can see. It shows thee has a kind heart for all of God's little creatures."

There was no laughing after that; so Daniel kept on with his stories.

Of course he told them to his chum, Henry Miller. Henry lived a mile or so up the creek. He was one year older. His folks were Quakers. He went to the woods for his cows. And he had been taught Hiding, Tracking, Sounds, Calls, and Directions.

The boys practiced these lessons together. They didn't want to forget them. And they knew perfectly well that they didn't dare to forget them. They wanted to come out of the woods alive.

2. Birds and Roses

Daniel told Henry he was sure animals talked to one another. "They make sounds and motions," he said. "I'm beginning to understand them myself."

"I wish I could," said Henry.

"They have to know you real well before they'll talk before you. They tell their secrets now while I'm sitting there. They plan their nests and choose their trees."

"Do birds know who you are? I mean, do they know it's you?"

"Of course they do. I proved it to find out. When I sit on the log, they're quiet now and friendly. But when I took Bessie there the other day, they scolded and worried until I had to take her home."

"Well! Well!" said Henry.

"I found out something else, too. They like bright colors."

"A bird can't tell colors, Dan!"

"They know when cherries are red, don't they?"

"Well—yes—I suppose so."

"They know when roses are in bloom, too. I

found that out yesterday. I stopped to look at a wild-rose bush. The roses were all out and they were pink and lovely."

Henry nodded. "They are pretty when they're blooming. I like to look at them."

"You're not the only one, Henry. A turtledove flew into the bush to get a good look."

"Oh, come now, Daniel. She just happened to light there."

"Wait a minute. She looked at a rose. Then she looked at me. Then she looked at the rose again. And, just as true as I'm standing here, she cooed at that rose."

"Cooed at the rose!" exclaimed Henry.

"She did. And it was the sweetest sound I ever heard."

"For goodness sake!" cried Henry. "I never heard of such a thing in all my life! Think of that, will you! A bird cooing at a rose!"

3. A Strange-Acting Crow

One day Daniel saw a crow fly to a tree near his log. There was nothing strange about that, but it was strange the way that bird acted.

He turned his head this way and that. He looked to the north. He looked to the south. He looked east and he looked west. He looked above. He looked below. Then suddenly he darted down to a sapling. Again he looked north, south, east and west. Again he looked above and below.

"What is he up to?" Daniel thought. "It looks like he's fixing to do something and he doesn't want any other crow to see him."

The crow darted down to a bush and again looked in every direction. Daniel could see him plainly now. The afternoon sun shone on his glistening black feathers and head.

Then Daniel saw some shining thing in his beak. "Why, it's a piece of metal!" he said to himself. "He's been looking about for a place to hide it."

Now the crow flew down to the ground and went under the bush. Daniel heard the rustling of dry leaves for a moment. Then the bird came out, and again looked all about.

The shining bit of metal was gone!

The crow darted to a bush and again looked in every direction.

4. The Rabbit and the Robins

One day Daniel saw something that made him laugh. But he laughed to himself. He was too wise to make any kind of a noise in the woods. He knew that would spoil everything.

Two robins were grubbing for worms in a grassy spot. They were tending strictly to business. They watched, they listened, they grubbed.

Suddenly a young rabbit peeped out of the bushes. He looked at the robins. Then he looked at Daniel on the log.

Now Daniel and the rabbit were friends. The boy knew where the rabbit's nest was. The rabbit knew the boy was to be trusted. He belonged in the woods. He was one of them.

The cottontail hopped toward the robins. They gave him one look only and went on grubbing. Worms were their business.

The rabbit was disappointed. He wanted to play, so he hopped closer. Still the birds didn't look at him. Then he began running around them in a circle.

"He's determined to make them look," Daniel thought.

The robins did look but they didn't move. They just stood there in the center. And around

Around and around them the rabbit ran, faster and faster.

and around them ran the rabbit, faster and faster, closer and closer. "A little too close," Daniel thought.

Daniel was right. Suddenly the birds rushed, their wings spread, their heads down, their tails up.

The rabbit thought the birds were ready to play with him. So he stopped running and hopped toward them.

The next thing he knew, strong wings were beating him. Strong bills were nipping him. Strong claws were tearing out his fur.

He didn't know how to fight them, for he had neither wings nor bills nor claws. Suddenly he remembered his mother's strong hind feet. He'd been punished by them more than once.

Quick as a wink, he struck out at the birds and knocked them flat with one good kick. Before they could get up he was gone. He went into the brush so fast Daniel could see only the white of his "cottontail."

The two robins were now up and busy with their feathers. They cleaned them and oiled them and smoothed them, chattering angrily. They finally calmed down and at last Daniel thought they were laughing.

"I'd better not tell the folks that story," he said, as he went home. "They wouldn't believe it. I wouldn't believe it myself if I hadn't seen it."

5. The Woodpecker and the Squirrels

Up in the fork of an old hickory tree was a squirrel's nest. Daniel had seen young squirrels peeping out when he was looking for nuts.

"It's a good strong tree," he told Henry. "The nuts will be good."

"We'll get them then, just as soon as they are ripe."

"They're ripe now. They're falling."

"I can go Saturday. I'll come by for you."

But the very next day Daniel wasn't so sure the nuts would be good. He heard a woodpecker tapping in the hickory.

Suddenly his keen ears noticed the sound of that "peck, peck, peck, peck." It wasn't the dull sound given by rotting wood. It was the sharp, hard sound of strong healthy wood.

Daniel was puzzled. "That bird knows those sounds better than I do. Why doesn't he go where he'll find worms?"

The woodpecker didn't go; he kept on tapping. So Daniel decided the tree must have a decayed spot after all.

Then a squirrel ran down the trunk to a limb just above the bird. She barked and chattered and scolded. But the woodpecker kept on pecking.

Another squirrel came running down the trunk and joined the first squirrel. Now both

Then a squirrel ran down the trunk to a limb just above the bird.

barked and chattered and scolded. But the woodpecker kept on pecking.

Again they barked. Again he pecked. Again they scolded. Again he pecked. They chattered. He pecked.

"I could tell he was teasing them," Daniel told

Henry. "I could see him peep up at them, wait a minute and then peck again."

"How did it end?" asked Henry.

"Well, all of a sudden both squirrels began to pick hickory nuts. Then they dropped them on the woodpecker."

"Daniel!"

"It's the truth, Henry. Those squirrels worked faster than I could. They had nuts falling so fast it looked like a hail storm. The woodpecker had to give up and fly away."

"Ha! Ha!" laughed Henry. "When did you make that one up?"

"I didn't make it up."

"But squirrels don't throw nuts. Animals can't throw things."

"Don't monkeys throw cocoanuts?"

"Why—yes—that's what people say."

"Then why couldn't squirrels throw hickory nuts?"

"Well, I can't say they couldn't, Daniel."

V

MEETING INDIAN BOYS

1. Daniel Meets Wolf

DANIEL wasn't satisfied with his turkey gobble. So one day he went to the cornfield to practice it. He went clear to the edge of the woods so his brothers wouldn't hear him. They liked to tease him about his howls and hoots and gobbles.

He sat on a stump and went to work. He gobbled high; he gobbled low; he gobbled loud and he gobbled soft. But still he wasn't satisfied.

He knew if he gobbled exactly right a wild turkey in the woods would answer him. He knew also he'd be the proudest boy alive if that happened. His brothers couldn't laugh at him then. They'd never had a turkey answer them.

Getting that call exactly right was almost impossible. It had to be a certain tone. The tone had to be a certain length and a certain clearness.

Daniel had the tone in his mind. He'd been listening to gobblers and hens for months.

"I'll try once more," he thought, "and I hope I'll get it right this time. I'll put my mind on it." Then after a moment or so, he gobbled.

Almost at once came a gobble from the woods!

Daniel jumped up and shouted with joy. "I've done it!" he cried. "I've done it!" He started to turn a handspring but he stopped before he began.

An Indian boy sprang out from a bush close by and came running toward him. He was about Daniel's age and he was tall and slender and handsome. He was smiling, too, in a friendly way.

"How!" said the boy. "Me—Wolf."

"How!" said Daniel. "Me—Daniel."

Then Wolf gobbled.

"Oh!" cried Daniel. "So it was you!"

Wolf nodded and laughed. Daniel laughed. Then they were friends.

"Me wait. Father go—take horse—shop."

Daniel nodded. "I understand, blacksmith shop."

"Yes," said Wolf, "that it. Moccasins for horse."

Daniel wanted to laugh but he didn't. His mother had taught him good manners.

Wolf pointed to a row of stumps. "Me like play—that—game you make."

"Stumps?" asked Daniel. He was astonished.

Wolf nodded and smiled brightly.

"How do you know about it?"

"Watch one time—see."

There was a long row of stumps at the edge of the field. They had been dragged out of it and

They shouted and laughed as they ran through this crooked path.

dumped. So they made a zigzag row, some here, some there, but all close together.

It took a good deal of twisting to run between them. It always made Bessie dizzy. But it didn't make Daniel dizzy nor Wolf, either. They shouted and laughed as they ran through this crooked path. And they kept it up until Wolf's father came.

He smiled at Daniel as he stopped his horse. "Boy—good?" he asked.

"Yes," said Daniel. "We played."

Wolf jumped to the horse from a stump. "Come again!" said Daniel. "Come again!"

"You come Indian Town," said Wolf. Then he rode away behind his father. But he didn't forget to turn and smile and wave his hand before they disappeared in the woods.

That evening the Boones heard all about Wolf. Daniel couldn't talk about anything else: how smart Wolf was and how friendly.

"Of course he'd be friendly," said Mr. Boone. "He's a Delaware. That tribe has always treated us well. Their village isn't so far from here—a half-day's ride."

"I'd like to go," said Daniel. "Wolf asked me to come."

"I'm going that way soon to buy a cow," said Israel. "I'll take you along."

"No," said Mrs. Boone. "Daniel must not go there until he knows Wolf better."

"Why, I know him now, Mother. He's just like Henry and the other boys I play with. I can't see a bit of difference."

"There is a difference and thee will find it out in time."

"But he wants to play with me!"

"Then let him come here. Thee cannot go to Indian Town."

Daniel was disappointed but he said no more. Quaker children didn't argue with their parents.

2. Nuts and Arrows

There was still no teacher for the little settlement of Exeter. The parents were sorry, but it was nice to have the children free just now.

It was late autumn and time to gather nuts.

Day after day piles of nuts

This was the children's work but it was very important. Nuts were a part of their winter food and great piles must be gathered.

There would be times when hunters could not hunt because of deep snows. And then, instead

were stored away for the winter.

of venison or bear steaks, there would be walnuts, butternuts, hazelnuts, hickory nuts and beechnuts. Even acorns were gathered for the hogs: bushels and bushels of them.

Sometimes the children didn't have far to go. Nut trees were in their front yards and back yards, and on the edge of clearings. So day after day piles of nuts were stored away for the winter.

It was work but it was fun, too. It was exciting to walk through dry and crackly leaves. It was exciting to climb the great walnuts and hickories, shake the branches and watch the nuts fall.

Daniel thought it was exciting just to look at the woods. The trees flamed with color: orange, yellow, brown, green, and red. It was so beautiful he wished it might last forever.

One day the older boys of the settlement went after butternuts. The trees grew on the river bank some four miles away. They took their lunches and planned to have a picnic.

They met at the blacksmith shop. It was in the center of the settlement and handy for everyone.

There was now a new smith—Pete McGuire. His feet had been hurt by a falling boulder so his hunting days were over.

Today he had a good deal to say to the boys. He said they'd most likely find Indian children picking nuts, too. He told them to be careful how they treated them.

"They use nuts for food in the winter just as we do. They have a right to all the nuts they want. Let them have more than their share. There must be no quarrels."

"That's what my father said!" cried Jim Cross.

"So did mine!" cried the others.

"We don't want the whole tribe mad at us because of a few nuts," said the smith. "Now go along and don't forget what I told you. No quarrels."

It didn't take the boys long to reach the Schuylkill River. Four miles were just a nice walk for those strong young pioneers. Nor did it take them long to fill their large skin bags with butternuts, and to eat their cornbread and dried-meat lunches.

They hurried with everything so they would have longer to play. Some six boys were having a race down on the shore now. Daniel and Henry were watching them from the top of the bank.

"I hope they won't run into those nut bags," said Daniel. "Do you see them? They're close to the water."

Henry nodded. "I guess they belong to the Indians," he said.

"I know they do. I saw an Indian boy carry one down not long ago. A canoe will come for them. That's the way they do."

"Then the Indian children are still picking nuts," said Henry.

"There they are!" exclaimed Daniel. "On the bank up the river, under those butternut trees."

Henry looked. "They're all boys; some big ones, too," he said.

"I'm glad they didn't come here," said Daniel. "Now I know we won't quarrel."

Just then came loud shouting and laughter from the shore. The boys turned quickly to look down.

"Oh!" cried Henry. "They've opened the bags! They're throwing the nuts out!"

"Stop that!" Daniel called.

"Stop it!" called Henry.

The boys on the shore paid no attention. They were throwing the nuts at each other now.

The Indian boys rushed to the bank and yelled angrily. The white boys laughed and threw nuts at them.

Suddenly an arrow flew through the air and

struck one of the bags. Then another arrow struck another bag.

There was silence now down on the shore. Six boys stood there, afraid an arrow would strike one of them next.

Henry and Daniel were frightened. They feared their friends would be killed.

"Run!" screamed Daniel. "Run under the bank! They can't hit you there!"

The boys didn't move. They were afraid to run.

Now other boys came running and joined Daniel and Henry. They began to shout to the boys on the shore. They didn't know what they said, they were so excited.

More and more arrows were shot into the bags. At last every bag had been hit.

Some of the white boys on the bank covered their faces. They couldn't bear to see what would happen next.

Just then a canoe came around a bend. In it

were two Indian women. One held up her arm and motioned to the Indian boys. They went back into the woods at once.

The canoe landed. The squaw got out and went straight to the scared boys. "Pick up!" she said angrily.

They didn't have to be told again. They picked up and picked up until the bags were full.

"Put—canoe," said the squaw.

The boys obeyed. The squaw then motioned them to go. They scrambled up the bank somehow. Their legs were almost too weak to carry them.

"Come quick!" said Daniel when they got to the top. "We must get away from here."

Silently bags were lifted and swung over shoulders. Silently they all trudged homeward.

They couldn't talk; they were too worried. Would this cause trouble with the tribe? Would it bring the warriors down on their homes and families?

VI

INDIANS ON THE WARPATH

1. Exeter Gets Ready

THE morning after the picnic, the black-smith shop was crowded with men. There were settlers from up the creek, down the creek, and north from the Schuylkill River. Some were old settlers, some were new. But all were grave and anxious.

They were listening now to the smith who stood by his forge in his great leather apron and cap.

"Yes, gentlemen," said Mr. McGuire, "I reckon I do know these Delawares better than any of you. I've hunted with them for months at a time. I've lived in their villages and I've had them for friends."

"That's the reason we've come to you, Pete,"

said Jim Pierce. "We're all worried about that trouble over the nuts yesterday."

The others nodded their heads gravely.

"Well," said Pete slowly, "if the Indians want an excuse to attack us, this nut trouble will be as good as any."

"Why should they want an excuse?" asked a newcomer. "I thought the Delawares were friendly with you folks. I'd never have brought my family to these parts if I'd known there was danger of an Indian attack."

"Mr. Williams," said Pete, "do you honestly think Indians enjoy the sight of hundreds of white men in their forests? Do you think they enjoy looking at clearings and farms and cabins where they once hunted? Do you think they love us when they have to trudge twenty miles or more to find a deer?"

"Well, putting it that way, I suppose they don't," Joe Williams answered.

"Well," said Pete slowly, "if the Indians want an excuse to attack us, this trouble will be as good as any."

76

"They couldn't, down deep in their hearts," said Lester Cross.

"Of course they couldn't," said Pete. "It wouldn't take much to make them attack us. It's bound to happen sometime."

"Aye, it is!" said Henry Dixon. "Do you think we'd better get ready for an attack, Pete?"

"I do, Henry. And if I had children I'd make sure they knew how to throw a tomahawk."

The settlers acted at once. By noon scouts were watching all trails. The fort was being made ready. Guns were being cleaned and loaded. Food was being cooked and children were practicing on targets.

These children had to be at least nine years old, for they had to practice with hunting knives first. Afterward they threw tomahawks. They had to hit the center of the target, too. Some children were punished if they didn't.

It wasn't a game. It was a matter of getting an Indian before he got you.

All the Boone children practiced, from young lady Sally down to nine-year-old Daniel. And it wasn't long until he was better than any of them, except Israel. He hit center oftener.

"Dan's got an eye for aiming," said John.

"He'll beat me if he keeps on hitting the bull's-eye nine times out of ten," said Israel.

"Dan's really getting ready for Indians," said Sally.

"All Exeter is getting ready," said Mr. Boone gravely.

2. "Run to the Fort!"

Early one morning just four days after the picnic, a scout rode up to the Boone cabin. He pounded on the door without getting off his horse.

"Run to the fort!" he cried. "They're coming!" Then he galloped away to warn others.

In five minutes the Boone family was on the way. They carried guns, ammunition, food, clothing, bedding, kettles and water buckets. Mr. Boone was in front with his gun. Israel was last with his. Their keen eyes watched for enemies all along the trail.

Their keen eyes watched for enemies all along the trail.

The fort was more than a mile away but they reached it safely. Some families were already there. Others came in a short time. The last one was the rider who had warned them.

Pete closed and bolted the heavy door. Men stood at loopholes with their guns. Boys stood back of them to pass the ammunition.

Daniel stood near his father. Henry stood near his.

The six nut-throwers wanted to help everyone. They knew they had brought this trouble upon the settlement and they were brokenhearted. Everyone felt sorry for them.

Some of the women were tearing sheets into strips for bandages. There were sure to be wounded men.

Others had built a fire. Others were swinging a great iron kettle over it. Boiling water would be needed for the wounded.

Then it was that the women suddenly discovered a terrible thing. There was no water to put in the kettle! It had been forgotten!

Was it too late? Could they get to the spring?

It was close by but Indians might be hiding there.

Daniel heard them talking and he made up his mind quickly. "I'll go!" he cried.

"No!" cried Ned Pierce, one of the nut-throwers. "I'm going!" Then he seized a bucket, lifted the bar from the door and ran out of the fort.

The other five nut-throwers didn't wait one instant. They also seized buckets and followed Ned.

3. The Warriors Come

Again Pete McGuire closed the strong door and bolted it. Everyone feared the boys wouldn't come back.

"Ned wanted to make up for the trouble he's caused," said Mrs. Pierce.

"So did Jim," said Mrs. Cross.

"Paul said he was going to do something for the settlement," said Mrs. McDonald.

"John wanted to do something, too," said Mrs. Jones.

"So did Arthur," said Mrs. Dixon. "He wondered what he could do. He'll be glad he tried to get water even if he's captured."

"They're all fine boys," said Mr. Boone. "It was only a prank. No one blames them."

Lookouts stood at peepholes and watched. Suddenly one of them shouted. "The boys are coming back! They're running! The Indians are after them!"

"I'll open the door," said Pete.

"No, you can't!" cried the lookout. "The warriors are too close to them. You can't even fire!"

There was a moment of silence. Every man's finger was on the trigger, ready to fire when the signal was given.

Then the lookout shouted again: "They're here—at the door—warriors close behind!"

A voice outside called, "Open the door, Pete!"

"That's Ned's voice!" cried Mr. Pierce.

"I'll take a look," said Pete as he hurried to a peephole in the door. And while he was looking everyone was thinking of those brave boys out there.

What would the Indians do with them? Why did they let the boys call Pete? Was it a trick to get the door open so the Indians could rush in?

Then Pete turned a puzzled face to them. "I can't understand it," he said. "The warriors are smiling."

"Are the boys smiling?" asked Mr. Pierce.

"No, they look scared."

"It's a trick!" cried a man.

"Aye!" said the others.

Now an Indian voice called, "Pete—we friends—come see!"

Pete peeped out again. This time he was smiling when he turned. "Good news!" he called. "The warriors have laid down their guns.

They're coming up with lifted hands. I'm going out to talk with them."

Then he opened the door and went out. The six boys came into the fort and the Indians paid no attention. They were talking and laughing with Pete.

In a few minutes he was back at the door. "They're laughing about our scare, folks. They didn't come to attack us. They came to save us from an attack."

"Save us!" cried Mr. Dixon. "What do you mean?"

"They had heard that those fierce savages over the mountains were on the warpath, and would attack this settlement."

"Oh!" cried a frightened woman. "Are those savages coming?"

"No," said Pete. "They've gone back. A Delaware scout has just come with the news."

"Heaven be praised!" said a Quaker.

"Aye!" said the others.

"Friends," said Squire Boone, "we must show our gratitude to these splendid Indians. What can we do, Pete?"

"Give them a feast," said Mr. McGuire. "Nothing will please them more."

It was almost dark before the feast was over. Then happy Indians faded into the forest. Happy families went back to their cabins. And six happy boys felt they had been forgiven.

VII

FRONTIER BOYS

1. Daniel's Work

ALL summer the Boone boys had a new helper on the farm, their young brother Daniel. He had been ten last November and was old enough now to work.

He helped cut down trees, pull up stumps and dump them in a zigzag row. He plowed, raked, hoed, sowed seed and pulled weeds.

He went after the cows and now he helped to milk them. He learned to make butter and cheese.

He stirred the boiling soap in the great iron kettle out in the yard. He melted grease and poured it into candle molds.

He planted vegetables and took care of them.

He gathered greens—wild mustard, dandelion, and wild cabbage.

He picked wild berries in the summer and nuts in the fall.

He helped tap maple trees and boil down the sap.

He helped tap maple trees and boil down the sap.

He learned how to put meat on a long forked stick and roast it over the fire.

"Now I'll know how to roast a piece of venison when I'm on a long hunt," he told Henry. "You have to know how to do everything if you live in the woods alone."

He learned how to take care of his father's horses and he learned how to ride them.

"Why, he rides like an Indian boy," said Israel.

His brothers were watching him one evening. "Why, he rides like an Indian boy," said Israel. "Look at him, bareback, and guiding with his knees!"

"He's riding like a whirlwind," said John. "I'm afraid he'll fall."

"There's no danger of that," said Israel. "His muscles are as hard as rock."

"That's what farm work has done for him," said Sam.

"He's tough," said Israel proudly.

"Aye!" cried the others just as proudly.

2. Frontier Games

Daniel wasn't the only boy who had worked that summer. They all had plowed, chopped, pulled stumps and weeded. So, by fall, there was a bunch of hard and tough Exeter youngsters. Every one of them was proud of his muscles and his strength. A weakling wouldn't last a day at hunting and trapping. They didn't intend to be weaklings.

When autumn came they had time to play a little but their games were all games of strength. They wouldn't play anything else. They wrestled, ran races and had target matches.

Daniel was too light to be a good wrestler. He was thrown almost every time. But he could run faster than any of them.

"Why, he's here and then he's gone," said Paul McDonald.

"He runs like a streak of lightning," said Ned Pierce.

"No Indian will ever catch him," said Jim Cross.

"Hooray! Hooray!" they all yelled when Daniel reached the goal first.

He was best at target throwing, too. He used to hit the center often. Now he hit it almost every time. And he threw with much greater force since his muscles had grown so strong.

All the boys were proud of him. Not one even thought of being jealous.

"Hooray!" they yelled every time Daniel hit dead center. "Hooray for Daniel!"

Sometimes they went to the Schuylkill River for swimming and canoe races. And sometimes they forgot to get home in time for supper.

But not a single mother ever complained of that. Their boys might have to swim across rivers to get away from Indians. Their very lives might depend on how well they could paddle a canoe.

Daniel was among the best at both sports. There didn't seem to be any best; they were all so good.

"Boys," said Pete McGuire, "it would take an Indian to beat you." He had gone to the river one day to watch them.

"Are Indians better?" asked Daniel anxiously.

"Are they?" asked half a dozen others.

Pete smiled. "Well," he said slowly, "I'm going to tell you the gospel truth." He stopped.

Sometimes they went to the Schuylkill

The boys waited anxiously. It would be a terrible thing if Indians could beat them.

Pete continued: "Yes, sir, I'm going to tell you the gospel truth. They aren't."

"Hooray!" yelled the boys.

River for swimming and canoe races.

That night a bunch of frontier youngsters bragged a little at home. But none of their folks minded that. They wanted to hear that their boys were better than Indian boys at swimming and canoeing.

3. Daniel's Secret

Late one afternoon Daniel and Henry were going home from a target match. They always went together as far as the creek, and they always talked things over as they went along.

"You hit center every single time today,"

"You hit center every single time today," said Henry. "I wish I were as good as you. I wish I were half as good."

"I wish Wolf could see me throw," said Daniel.

"I wish he could, too. I wonder why he hasn't been back."

"He's been away on a buffalo hunt. The whole village went. Someone told Israel. I'm going there when they get back."

"I thought your mother said you couldn't."

said Henry. "I wish I were as good as you."

"Oh, she's afraid of Indians, but I'm not. Are you?"

"Well—I've heard lots of scary things about them."

"So have I, but I don't believe them. I think they're just like us. I know Wolf is. The only difference is his skin and you can't blame him for that, can you?"

"Of course not," said Henry.

"What's the difference whether your skin is white or red?"

"Well, I don't know," said Henry. "I just kinda like white skin better."

"I wouldn't care if mine was red," said Daniel.

"But then you'd be an Indian!"

"I wouldn't care if I was."

"Why, Dan'l!"

"I wouldn't. Henry, if I tell you something will you promise you won't tell?"

"I promise. What is it?"

"I'm going to Indian Town if I have to run away."

"You'd better not, Daniel. How do you know they'd want you?"

"They would when they saw me hit the target. They like white boys who can do things. Pete told me that."

"Your folks would go after you."

"I'd get Wolf to hide me."

"How long are you going to stay?"

"Oh, a year or two."

"You'll get homesick away from your folks all that time, Dan'l."

"Maybe I'll stay only a month or so."

"When are you going to run off?"

"I'm just waiting for the tribe to get back. I've had my things ready for a week."

"You won't be taking your Sunday suit, will you? That cloth one your father wove?"

"No-o, I guess not. I wouldn't be going to

meeting any. I thought I'd just take my other shirt."

"That's enough," said Henry.

The boys had reached the creek now, so they parted.

"Don't tell anyone!" called Daniel as he went his way.

"I won't!" promised Henry as he went his way.

VIII

SURPRISES

1. Daniel Surprised by Mother

THAT very evening Israel said he needed another horse for the farm.

"I don't know where you'll get one," said his father. "The settlers haven't any to sell."

"Mr. Pierce has just bought one from the Indians," said Israel.

"Oh!" cried Daniel. "Have they come back from their buffalo hunt?"

"Just last week," Israel answered. Then he turned to his father. "They brought back some wild horses. That's why they're selling some of their old ones."

"We'd better get one right away," said Mr. Boone. "Could you go tomorrow?"

"Yes, I guess the boys can get along without me for one day."

"Of course," said Sam.

"We'll try," said John.

"I suppose the Indians will take skins for pay," said Mr. Boone. "They always have."

"Mr. Pierce paid them with skins."

"We have some good furs," said Mr. Boone. "I've been looking them over."

"I'll get a bundle ready tonight, Father."

"Don't let those Delawares beat you on the trade. They're sharp."

"I know they are," said Israel with a smile. "I've traded with them before and got the worst of the bargain."

"I wish I could go," Daniel thought. "But Mother wouldn't let me. I might run away—no use to run away and walk if I can ride—if I went with Israel I might stay—I'd hide in a cave or somewhere——"

"Dan'l!" said Sally sharply. "Are you asleep?"

Then Daniel noticed that everyone was looking at him and smiling.

"Mother's been trying to talk to you," said Bessie.

"What was thee thinking about?" asked Mrs. Boone.

"Oh, I don't know; Indian Town, I guess."

"That's what I've been talking about. I said thee could go."

"Go?" cried Daniel. "Go? With Israel?"

"Yes, thee is older now. Thee understands Indians better. And thee seems to like this Wolf."

"He's crazy about all of them," said Sam, smiling. "He didn't take his eyes off those warriors that day at the fort."

"I don't blame him," said Mr. Boone. "They were handsome fellows."

"I liked their color," said Daniel.

"Ha, ha!" laughed the boys.

"Ha, ha!" laughed the girls.

"I did," said Daniel. "I wouldn't care if I were red."

"You'll turn into an Indian if you don't watch out," said John.

"Seems to me his skin is a little red now," said Sally.

"No more teasing," said Mr. Boone. "Daniel has worked hard this summer. A little trip will be good for him. You may ride my horse, Dan. You know how to manage her. And, Israel, you boys must get an early start."

"Yes, sir," said Israel.

"Yes, sir," said Daniel.

2. Daniel Surprised by Village

The two brothers ate their breakfast by candle light. Then they put on their coonskin caps, took the lunch their mother had packed, mounted their horses and started to Indian Town.

They had to ride slowly, for the trail was narrow, and rough with great roots.

About ten o'clock they stopped to rest and water their horses and to eat their lunch.

"Why don't we wait and eat with the Indians?" asked Daniel.

"They don't eat when we do, Dan. They have only two meals a day. Their breakfast is at eleven and it will be over before we can get there. We can't wait for their second meal. We'll be on our way home."

"Maybe *I* won't," Daniel said to himself.

They rode on and on. About noon the trail became wider and smoother.

"We're almost there, Dan'l. We'll see the town in another minute."

Then, there it was—in a grove of magnificent old trees on the bank of the Schuylkill River.

"Why, it's beautiful!" cried the boy.

"It's a large village. There must be some fifty houses."

Daniel was surprised at the size of the houses. "I thought they lived in cabins," he said, "like ours."

"No, they build long houses. Each one holds three or four families."

"I wish I could live here."

"You wouldn't like it very long."

"Why wouldn't I?"

"Oh, Indians are different. We can't understand their ways."

"I would," said Daniel to himself. "I don't think they're a bit different."

"Look at the canoes down there!" exclaimed Israel. "There's a fleet of them, two hundred or more."

Now a tall, slender boy came running out of the grove to meet them.

"Wolf!" cried Daniel. "How!"

"How!" cried Wolf. "Know you come with brother. Scout saw long time." Then he smiled and laughed and said he'd show them where to tie their horses. With that he went ahead, walking lightly.

"Did you hear that?" Daniel whispered to Israel. "They knew we were coming."

"That shows they're always watching. I expect we'll learn a good many things before we leave."

"Here, good place!" Wolf called.

The horses were tied to saplings. Then Israel went to see the chief and Wolf took Daniel toward a large clearing.

"Pony race—for you, Dan'l—get up quick—when scout see."

Daniel was delighted. Wolf was doing all this for him. Wouldn't he have something to tell the boys when he went back! But he wasn't going back—not right away.

3. Daniel Surprised by Wolf

The two boys had reached the field. Some twelve Indian boys stood by their ponies, waiting. They all looked at Daniel and smiled.

"Wait here," Wolf said. "I go. There my pony. See? Old brave hold."

Presently this old brave gave a signal. Then the boys leaped to their ponies and the race was on. They rode bareback and guided with their knees. They were splendid riders. Daniel could see that from the start.

A crowd of children was watching. They yelled and shouted and jumped about just like so many white children, Daniel thought.

Then Daniel began to yell and shout, too, for now Wolf's pony was in the lead.

And Wolf's pony stayed in the lead and won. Daniel rushed up to Wolf at once.

"I'm so glad you won!" he cried. "You're a wonderful rider!"

"Of course," said Wolf proudly. "White boy no ride good bareback!"

"Why, that's the way we always ride," said Daniel. "We guide with our knees, too."

He wasn't bragging. He thought Wolf would be pleased to know this, but Wolf was not pleased. The Indian boy frowned and made an ugly noise.

The old brave now told Daniel he could run in the foot race. So Daniel took his place in the line.

The brave gave a signal and the race began. Daniel won it easily. He was far ahead of the others at the end.

He thought Wolf would be proud of him, but Wolf wouldn't look at him. Daniel couldn't understand it. He thought Wolf was angry at some Indian boy.

A target was now put up and every boy was

allowed three throws with a tomahawk. The Indian boys threw first.

Not one of them hit the target dead center, not even Wolf.

Daniel threw last and hit dead center every time. He expected to hear shouts of praise and clapping. But there was only silence.

And now Daniel noticed that the boys were all glaring at him. There wasn't a friendly smile anywhere, not even from Wolf. He was worse than the others. His dark eyes glittered with hate.

Then he shook his tomahawk at Daniel and ran from the field. That seemed to excite the other boys. They began to yell angrily and run about.

Daniel was frightened. He didn't know what to do.

"Come," said a low voice. "Follow—quick!" It was the old brave. He led Daniel into the brush quickly and down to the river shore.

"Go—now—canoe—Wolf maybe shoot." He pushed a canoe into the water. Daniel stepped into it and lifted the paddle.

"Keep middle river—all time—no go near shore—Wolf shoot from woods."

"Keep middle river—all time—no go near shore—Wolf shoot from woods. No stop till see cabin—settler there."

"I know," said Daniel. "The Dixons live there."

"Wait—cabin—brother. Tell now."

Then the old man went back into the brush and Daniel was alone on the river.

IX

WOLF WAS JEALOUS

1. "Daniel Must Go Back"

"THAT'S the way it was," said Daniel. "Wolf shook his tomahawk at me and ran away from the games."

Daniel was telling his story over for the fourth time. First he had told it to the Dixons who lived in the first cabin on the river.

Next he told it to Israel who came there later leading two horses.

Then he had told his folks, and now he was telling it to Pete McGuire at the blacksmith shop.

Mr. Boone had taken Daniel there at once. "This is very serious," he had said to Mrs. Boone. "Pete can tell us what to do."

Mr. McGuire seemed to think it was serious,

too, for his face grew graver and graver as he listened. And his voice was grave when he spoke.

"Wolf was jealous of you, Daniel. Indians are like that. They're always jealous if a white man beats them in games. I found that out when I first went to live with them."

"They're not jealous if a white man beats them at hunting," said Squire.

"No, that seems to be all right. But it's different with games. They're very proud of their strength. They can't bear to think a white man is stronger. I found I had to lose more games than I won. At least, I did if I wanted to live."

"Was it that bad, Pete?"

"It was, Squire. Daniel, it won't be safe for you to go about any for a while."

"Can't I go after the cows?"

"No. You can't even go out to the barn. Wolf might be hiding close by."

"But Daniel has to live here, and he has to go about. What are we to do?"

"Well, knowing Indians the way I do, I'd say there was only one thing Daniel could do. He must go back to Indian Town."

"Go back!" exclaimed Squire.

"Yes, and play games again and this time he must lose."

"That would be like putting his head in the lion's mouth. Wolf could shoot him before the games begin."

"Wolf won't have a chance. I'm going to see the chief about that young rascal and I'm going today. He must have a guard. They must watch him day and night."

Squire shook his head. "It isn't likely the chief will punish Wolf."

"I think he will. The chief's a smart man and he doesn't want any trouble with the settlers. He knows what will happen if Daniel is harmed."

"Every white man in the country will arm and march against the village," said Squire Boone.

"Everyone," Pete agreed. "That's why I'm almost certain I can count on the chief. But keep Daniel inside till I get back."

"I can't stay in all the time," said Daniel.

"You'll have to," said his father. "I'll not have you taking any chances, not with that Indian boy loose in the woods."

"Your father is right, Daniel. Don't step outside unless one of your brothers is with you and he must have his gun."

"I'll see to it," said Squire.

"I'm going at once. You'll see me sometime tomorrow and I hope I'll bring good news."

2. Hands Seize Daniel

Five days had passed and Mr. McGuire had not returned. The Boones were worried. What had happened? Maybe he himself was a prisoner. Maybe the chief wasn't so friendly to white men after all. Wolf might be free and even now waiting close by to shoot an arrow or fire a gun.

Daniel wasn't allowed out of the cabin unless a brother was with him. That brother always carried a gun.

The boy thought he couldn't stand it another day. His legs ached for lack of running. His arms ached for lack of chopping and throwing. So the night of the fifth day he slipped out.

When everyone was asleep, he crept down the ladder, went across the room below, lifted the door latch quietly and went out.

It was great to be outside! He'd just take a walk down to the creek. Wolf wasn't likely to be around at night.

There was a full moon. It shone on the sycamores and made them look like ghosts. The poplars looked like trees of silver with crowns of silver leaves.

"It's like fairyland," the boy whispered.

He reached the creek bank and there he saw the loveliest picture of all. The moon was shining into the creek. It made a pathway of light across the water, a pathway of golden ripples.

Daniel stood there gazing at it. He couldn't get enough; he couldn't leave. He didn't hear a soft *pad, pad* behind him. He didn't see a dark form coming nearer and nearer.

Suddenly a hand grasped his shoulder! And quick as a flash Daniel sprang back and ran for the cabin.

He could hear the *pad, pad* plainly now. He knew the sound. It was moccasined feet and they were pursuing him.

He was thankful the door latch was up. He might escape—it wasn't much farther.

Then two strong hands seized him and held him fast.

"What do you mean running away from me?" asked the voice of Pete McGuire.

"Oh!" cried Daniel. "I thought you were an Indian."

Pete laughed. "I couldn't call you; I was afraid I'd wake your folks. That's why I followed you."

"What kept you so long?"

"Why, the lowlands were flooded. The creek close to Indian Town was out of its banks. I had to wait till the water went down."

"What did the chief say?"

"Just what I thought he would. He agreed to everything. Wolf has been a prisoner for four days."

"I've been a prisoner, too."

"That's all over now, Dan'l. Tell your folks there'll be Indian games tomorrow at the village."

"Do I have to go?"

"Of course. The chief thought it was a good plan. We'll start early tomorrow morning. I'll be here by daylight."

"I'll be ready, sir."

"Israel must come along. He must say he wants to change his horse; he's not satisfied with the one he bought."

"He isn't," said Daniel.

"That makes it all the better," said Pete. Then he faded away into the fog. And Daniel went back to his bed in the loft.

3. Daniel Tries to Lose

The chief smiled at Daniel and said he was glad he had come again to the games. Then he himself took the visitors to the field.

This time there was a large crowd there: warriors, braves, squaws and children. They had all heard about Wolf and Daniel and they wanted to see what would happen.

Israel stood on one side of Daniel. Pete stood on the other. Both carried knives and tomahawks in their belts. They had left their guns in

Daniel saw the same old brave waiting to give signals.

the chief's house. Pete said the Indians didn't like visitors to carry guns about the village.

Daniel saw the same old brave waiting to give

signals. He saw Wolf with his father, but neither of them even looked at Daniel.

"He's still angry," Daniel whispered to Pete.

"They won't allow him to enter any of the games," said Pete. "That's the way Indians punish their children."

"Won't they let him enter the target match?" asked Daniel.

"Not unless you lose. And you're going to lose. Remember our plans, Dan'l."

"You said I could try to win the running race."

"Yes. And that's all."

"Don't get too far ahead in that," said Israel.

The games began and Daniel lost in everything at first. He did better in the running race. He won, but the second runner was close behind.

The target was now put up and Daniel was told to throw first.

"Pete," he whispered, "I'm afraid I'll just naturally hit center; my arm's used to it."

"It's not your arm. It's your eye. Don't look at center."

"Look at the edge of the target," whispered Israel.

Daniel took his place. The old brave gave him a tomahawk. Daniel threw and didn't even hit the target.

The next time he hit the edge.

The third and last time he hit close to center but not dead center.

Israel and Pete were watching Wolf closely. They saw his scowl disappear when Daniel missed the first time. The second miss, he began to smile. The third miss, he laughed aloud.

"He's all right now," said Pete. "You can look after your horse trade, Israel."

Now Wolf threw and he had good luck every

time. He hit close to center twice and dead center once.

He was so pleased he ran to Daniel and smiled and cried, "How, Dan'l!"

"How!" said Daniel. He smiled but it was a very small smile. He was glad that Israel came back just then and said they were ready to go.

Wolf followed them to the edge of the grove and waved as they rode away. "Come again!" he called.

After a time Pete spoke. "Well, you boys learned some more about Indians today."

"I did," said Daniel. "I learned that I'd rather play with Henry and Ned and the other boys. They don't get jealous."

X

AT THE SUMMER PASTURE

1. Bundles for the Boones

Mrs. Boone and Daniel were going away for the summer. They were taking the cows up to the new pasture land and they would stay there with them till fall.

Two pack horses stood close to the cabin door. Mr. Boone and Daniel were loading them. Sally and Bessie were bringing out bundles.

There were clothing and bedding. There were cooking things in a large skin bag. There were buckets and gourds in another.

"Be careful how you load the horses," said Mr. Boone. "The bundles on each side must balance."

"Can't I go along, Father?" asked Sally. "I've never seen the little cabin you built up there."

"I want to see it, too," said Bessie. "And I want to see the little milk house you built over the spring."

"I'm sorry, girls, but there's barely room in the cabin for the two bunks and a table. Besides, I need you here to keep house for me while your mother is away."

"I could go in her place," said Sally. "I can keep house for Dan'l and take care of the milk, too."

"I'm sure you could, Sally. But your mother thinks she must keep an eye on Daniel. She's afraid he'll go hunting and forget the cows."

"Oh!" cried Daniel eagerly. "Are you going to give me a gun?"

"I've told you you can't have a gun till you're twelve years old. A boy of ten isn't strong enough to stand the kick of a rifle. Many a young boy has been hurt that way."

"But I know how to shoot. I've gone hunting with Israel and Sam."

"They carried the guns, didn't they?"

"Yes, but I could have——"

"Of course, I know you think you could. Carrying a loaded gun over a rough trail is dangerous. Suppose you stumbled over roots and the gun went off?"

"I'd watch for roots."

"Maybe. Here, you must tie these ropes tighter. These bags have slipped down a bit. You take that side. I'll see to this."

There was silence for a moment as they worked at the ropes. Then Daniel thought of another argument.

"There's wild animals up there, Father. All the boys say so. They say they wouldn't go away off there without a gun."

"They wouldn't have anything to shoot but rabbits. This pasture is only five or six miles from here, and there are farms all around it. There are no wild animals."

"A wolf might get hungry and come after a calf," said Daniel.

"Your dog will warn you and your mother will do the rest. She can shoot as straight as any man."

"But she might be too busy and King might be asleep."

"Daniel! Not another word!"

"Yes, sir," said Daniel meekly.

"But, Father, you said Dan might go off hunting," said Bessie.

"I meant he'd hunt for animal tracks and wander off to trace them."

"He's always doing that," said Sally. "And when he gets back he doesn't know whether he's eating dinner or supper."

The others laughed, even Daniel. "Oh come

now, Sally," he said, "I never did that but two or three times."

"Once would be too often when you're watching a herd," said Mr. Boone.

"I guess Mother is the one to go after all," said Sally. "She'll keep you straight, Dan'l."

"Girls!" called Mrs. Boone from the cabin door. "Here are some more bundles!"

2. Daniel's Secret Weapon

Mrs. Boone and Daniel had been living at the pasture for more than a month now. Every week either Mr. Boone or one of the boys rode up for the day. They always brought fresh meat, game they had killed on the way, and they always took back a load of butter and cheese. A good part of this was to sell in the settlement. The Boones were thrifty; they made a penny when they could.

For two weeks now no one had come. It was

harvest time and everyone was busy on the farm. So there was no meat in the cool springhouse.

"I'd go hunting myself," said Mrs. Boone, "if I had time. I'm getting hungry for meat."

"So am I," said Daniel gravely. But he didn't feel grave. He was so full of joy he could have shouted. He thought there would be quite a lot of fresh meat in the springhouse by evening. But he couldn't tell his mother now; not until he was certain. It was a secret.

Henry Miller was the only one he had told— the day Henry came with John.

"How did you ever think of it?" Henry had asked. "Or did someone tell you about it?"

"No, I thought of it and made it."

"What kind of wood did you use?"

"Hickory. It has to be strong."

"Of course. But how did you make that knob on one end?"

"I dug up a sapling with its roots. Then I cut

off the branches and small roots. After that I trimmed the large roots to make a knob."

"That's what kills, isn't it?"

"It will if I can throw it right. I'm practicing on a target now. When I can hit the center every time, I'll be ready to begin on animals. I don't want to cripple anything, not even a bird."

"Of course not. I wouldn't either." Then Henry threw Daniel's weapon at the target. He was delighted. "Why, it slips right through your hands, doesn't it?"

"I polished it so it would."

That was two weeks ago. Daniel had practiced every day out in the pasture. And every day his aim grew better.

At last he was ready. He hadn't missed center for a week. And he could throw as fast as a gun could shoot—or at least as fast as he could load and shoot.

So one day, armed with his shining spear,

Hunter Daniel Boone went out to hunt. With his mighty arm he threw and not once did he miss his game.

So fast, so sudden, so hard was the blow the little animals fell instantly. He was surprised at his success.

"Why, it's a real weapon," he said. "I'd just as soon use it as a gun."

He took the game home that evening:

Two rabbits	Three pigeons
Two squirrels	One turkey
One chipmunk	One groundhog

"Well! Well! Well!" said his mother. "And you killed them with that knob?"

"Yes," said Daniel. "It was easy."

After that fresh meat hung in the springhouse every day. There was even enough to send back by the visiting Boones.

3. A Strange-Acting Indian

Daniel trained King to guard the herd. Then for several days he watched the dog secretly. Not once did King leave the cattle. So Daniel felt he could hunt for an hour or so every day.

He was always back in time to drive them to the cabin to be milked. Then he locked them in cowpens for the night.

His mother was pleased. "Dan'l, thee is a good herder. But does thee not get lonesome, all day long by thyself?"

"Why, I never even think of that, Mother. It doesn't seem to me that I'm alone."

"I think thee must truly love the quiet."

Daniel nodded. "I'll be sorry when we have to leave."

The boy found that his father was right about wild animals. He had never even seen the tracks of one. Then one day he came upon them suddenly in the woods—the footprints of a wolf.

They were fresh tracks, too, but he wouldn't try to follow them. He wasn't sure his knob could kill a wolf.

He turned to go back to the pasture when he heard the soft pad of feet. In another instant he was hidden behind a thick bush, listening. There was something queer about this sound. It would stop for a minute, then begin again. Stop—*pad, pad*. Stop—*pad, pad*. Closer and closer came the sounds.

Indians always walked quickly on the trail. There would be no white hunters here, for there wasn't any big game. It must be a wolf. He'd have to try to kill it. He'd run if he missed.

He grasped his spear. He stood and waited. Then suddenly he hid behind the bush again.

It wasn't a wolf he saw. It was an Indian, a strange-acting Indian. He walked slowly. His head was bent. His eyes were on the ground. He came to Daniel's hiding place and stopped. He drew his hunting knife from his belt. He seemed about to thrust it into the bush.

It was an Indian, a strange-acting Indian. . . . He drew his hunting knife.

Then Daniel jumped out. He faced the red man and held his spear up, ready to throw.

The Indian was astonished. He looked at Daniel. He looked at the spear. Then he threw back his head, opened his mouth and laughed and laughed and laughed.

Daniel saw he had nothing to fear, so he lowered his weapon.

The Indian now spoke. "You—Wolf's friend —no fear. Me Medicine Man. Get plants. Look, look, stop, stop. All time look. When see—take knife—dig, dig."

"Oh!" cried Daniel. Then he threw back his head, opened his mouth and laughed and laughed and laughed.

Presently the Medicine Man pointed to the bush where Daniel had hidden. "There—see— plants need make medicine."

Daniel looked. "It's yellow root," he said. "It's for sore eyes."

The Medicine Man was surprised. "You know?" he asked. "How use?"

"My mother boils the roots. She uses the yellow water. It will cure a bad cold in your eyes."

The Medicine Man nodded. "Do same way," he said. "Mother—Medicine Woman?"

"She could be. She knows what kind of plant to use for every kind of sickness. She knows where they grow, too."

"Ah! That good. Need boneset. No find. Look —look—never no find. Indians sick—cough— need boneset tea."

"I'll show you where it's growing. There's a large patch."

He led the way to the pasture and then to the boneset growing near the brook.

"You know herbs?" asked the Indian doctor.

"I know a good many. I'm going to learn all of them. I'll have to be my own doctor when I'm a hunter."

"You sick—come me. You hurt—come me. Take care you. You fine boy—make good Indian."

"I'll come, sir, but I won't bring this club with me."

"Please not. Scare me very much," said the

Medicine Man. He smiled at Daniel, and Daniel smiled at him.

They had now reached the patch of boneset and presently both were busy gathering the plants.

XI

DANIEL'S TWELFTH BIRTHDAY

1. Will Daniel Get a Gun?

IT WAS November second, 1746, and it was Daniel's birthday. He was twelve years old. Now he should get the gun his father had promised him. His brothers had received their guns when they were twelve.

But maybe he wouldn't after all. He knew his father didn't have the money to buy one. He was afraid he didn't have enough skins to trade.

Hunting had been bad all fall. It had turned cold early in October. There had been several bad snowstorms. A deep snow covered the ground now and it was still very cold.

The fur-bearing animals—beavers, foxes, martins and weasels—were hidden away in caves. If they came out, none of the hunters around Exeter had seen them.

It was their skins the traders wanted most. Daniel was afraid they wouldn't take deer skins for a gun; their fur wasn't thick enough. And, so far as he knew, deer skins were all his folks had.

His brothers had been hunting several times this fall but they had killed nothing but deer. At least that's all they mentioned.

So what chance had he to get a gun? No game, no skins. No skins, no gun. And to make things worse, some of the boys were coming to see his gun this morning.

He hoped the snow would keep them at home but he knew it wouldn't. Hadn't he walked miles through snow to see Joe's and Paul's new guns?

Well, he didn't have to be ashamed even if he didn't get his present. No one in Exeter had any money. They wouldn't have furs this year, either.

Daniel knew the gun should be on his stool at breakfast. That's the way it was on his brothers' birthdays. What would he do if it wasn't there? Should he act as if he hadn't expected one? Should he pretend he didn't care?

His mind was so full of these thoughts he couldn't dress. His fingers were all thumbs. He couldn't fasten his leggings.

"Dan'l!" called his mother. "Breakfast is ready!"

The boy tried to hurry. Everyone had to be in his place at the table for morning prayers. But now he had trouble with his moccasins. They had shrunk and he couldn't get them on.

"Dan'l!" called Bessie. "Hurry!"

So down the ladder he went with his moccasins in his hand. He looked at his stool. Then he smiled. Then he laughed aloud. It was there—a beautiful shining new gun!

He threw down his moccasins and picked up his gun. "Oh!" he cried. "Oh! It's a gun!"

"What did you expect?" asked Sally. "A piece of maple sugar?" Then she whispered, "I've got some for you."

Daniel rubbed the shining metal barrel. He rubbed the polished walnut wood of the stock.

Daniel rubbed the shining metal barrel. He rubbed the polished walnut wood of the stock. "It's beautiful," he said. "I'd rather have it than anything else in the world. You must have given a good many fine skins for it, Father."

"Your brothers found the skins."

"But I thought——"

"Ha, ha!" laughed Israel, Sam and John.

Now prayers were over. Breakfast had been eaten. Mr. Boone had gone to his loom. The older boys were starting to work.

"I'll be out to help," said Daniel, "just as soon as I can get my moccasins stretched."

"We can get along without you today," said Israel. "It's your birthday, isn't it?"

"Why don't you go hunting?" asked John.

"Well, I did kinda promise Henry I'd go."

"Before you got your gun?" teased Sam. "You took an awful chance, Dan'l."

The brothers went out smiling and Daniel

smiled, too, as he stretched his moccasins. He was so happy he had to smile. Everyone was so good to him.

He had just finished putting on his moccasins when his friends came—Henry, Ned, Jim, Paul, Joe and Arthur.

They were all older than Daniel and they all had their own guns. Of course they examined Daniel's gun carefully. Then they all said it was a fine gun.

Daniel was delighted. He knew it was a fine gun, but it was nice to know the boys knew it.

2. *The Wolf and the Deer*

Daniel and Henry went hunting that afternoon. The snow didn't keep them at home. It was covered with a crust of ice so thick they could walk on it.

"I'm afraid we won't find any game," said Henry. "It's too cold."

"It's been cold for a week," said Daniel. "They'll have to come out for food."

As Daniel talked, his keen eyes were darting this way and that. He seemed to see on all sides at once. Suddenly he stopped and pointed to the right. "Look! There's a deer!" he said softly. "She's in a snowdrift. It's a doe."

"Your eyes are better than mine, Dan. I can't see her."

They went nearer. "Oh! I see her now!" said Henry. "She's struggling to get out."

"Her hoofs were too sharp for the crust," said Daniel.

The deer was helpless. They could have shot her easily, but neither boy lifted his gun.

"I'd no more shoot a helpless animal than I'd shoot myself," said Daniel.

"I wouldn't either," said Henry. "Let's help her out."

"Of course."

The boys hurried toward the deer. Suddenly Daniel turned and walked the other way.

Henry was astonished. "Aren't you going to help the deer out?"

"S-sh!" whispered Daniel. "Look over there to the left!"

"I don't see anything. What is it?"

"A wolf! He's just coming out of the forest, over there by that big sycamore. He's trying to get to that deer. He knows she's caught. He thinks he'll get an easy dinner, but he won't."

"I see him now," said Henry. "He's a big fellow. You can shoot him. It's the first chance you've had to try your gun."

Daniel nodded. "I'll wait till he gets closer." Then he laughed softly. "Just look at him slide over the ice! Those big padded feet of his are as good as snowshoes."

Henry laughed softly. "He wouldn't trade them for sharp hoofs, would he?"

"Not much," said Daniel.

By this time the boys had hidden behind a tree and the wolf was close enough to shoot. But Daniel didn't shoot and the big beast came closer and closer.

"Why don't you shoot?" whispered Henry.

"I want to be sure he's in my range. I don't know just how far my gun will shoot."

Another minute passed, then another and another. Henry was getting nervous. The wolf was so close now they could see his red eyes.

Another minute passed. Henry was scared by this time. If Dan didn't shoot in another second he'd shoot. He'd have to.

Then Daniel shot, and the wolf fell. The boys drew their hunting knives and went running. They would make sure the wolf was dead, not just wounded.

One look and they were satisfied. The knives were put back into the sheathes hanging from their belts.

Then they hurried to the deer and helped her out. She sped away but she went up the creek this time. The ice had thawed at the edge and she could go through running water.

"She's showing good sense," said Daniel. "She knows better than to try the snow again."

"She had to learn. Maybe this is her first snow."

"I'm sure it is. She wasn't a year old."

After that the boys shot enough squirrels and rabbits for both families. When they knew they had enough, they stopped.

Frontier boys thought it was fun to hunt but they never hunted for fun. So Henry wasn't surprised when Daniel said that it was time to go home.

"My gun's done enough for the first time," he said. "And you haven't missed many shots yourself, Henry."

"If I only had your eyes, I wouldn't miss any, Daniel."

XII

READY TO MAKE HIS LIVING

1. Daniel Fails to Return

LATE one afternoon a man rode up to the Boone barn. "Israel! Sam! John!" he called.

There was no answer. Then the man rode to the cornfield and looked about. There was no one there. He returned to the barn, tied his horse and walked to the weaving-house.

To his great surprise there was no one there. He then went to the cabin and knocked at the door. Sally opened it. "Uncle John!" she cried. "Come in!"

In another minute Mrs. Boone was telling Mr. John Boone how glad she was to see him. Bessie was hanging his hat on a peg. Sally was hanging his knapsack on another peg.

Uncle John was Squire Boone's brother. He was a small man, like Squire. He had red hair like Squire's. His eyes were gray like Squire's, and he had the same fair complexion. He was jolly, too, like Squire. The whole family was glad when he came to visit them.

He didn't come often. He was a teacher in a large settlement near Philadelphia.

"Thee has come at a sad time, John," said Sarah. "Daniel has failed to come home from a hunt. We fear he is lost."

"Lost! Why, that boy couldn't get lost, Sarah."

"He has been gone two days and two nights. This will make the third day. Never before has he stayed away overnight."

"Are Squire and the boys looking for him?"

"Yes, and the neighbors. They started early this morning, at daybreak. Here it is almost dark and there is no word from them."

"They might have to search tonight," said Sally.

"They'll not quit until all hope is gone," said Mrs. Boone sadly.

"I can't believe Daniel is lost," said John again. "He's not the kind to get lost. He always knew what he was doing."

"Dan'l is smart," said Sally.

"He's smarter than I am," said Bessie proudly. "He can see things I can't see. He can hear things I can't hear."

"Wild animals are smart, too," said Mrs. Boone. "I've always been afraid of that——"

"Don't worry about it, Mother," said Sally gently. "The animal doesn't live that can spring quicker than Daniel."

Just then voices were heard outside, and a moment later Israel came into the cabin.

"We found him, Mother! We found him!"

"Alive?" The word trembled on her lips.

Israel nodded. "Alive," he said. "He had built a little hut with saplings and he was living in it."

"Alone?" asked Sally.

"Yes. He was getting his dinner when we found him. He was roasting venison over a fire. It was the smoke from his fire that showed us where he was."

"Where is he now?" asked Mrs. Boone. "Why doesn't he come? Has anything happened to him?"

"He's all right; he'll be here in a little while. He's putting his skins in a dry place. He has quite a bundle."

Then Israel noticed his uncle for the first time. "Uncle John!" he cried. "I am glad you have come. Dan will be glad, too. He was speaking of you on the way."

2. Daniel Has Decided

Pretty soon Squire and Samuel and Jonathan were shaking hands with Uncle John. Of course they all said they were very glad to see him.

Then Daniel came in. He tried to greet his uncle but his mother and sisters surrounded him. They hugged him and asked questions and said they were so glad he had been found.

"I wasn't lost," said Daniel. "I knew where I was all the time."

"But we expected thee home," said his mother. "We've been so worried about thee, Dan'l."

"I'm sorry," said Daniel. "I didn't think you'd worry. No hunter leaves good hunting. Every-one knows that."

"Thee is too young to stay in the woods all night alone, my son."

"I'm past thirteen, Mother. It's time I began to make my own living. I can do it, too. I've brought back some good furs."

"He had them stretched out to dry all around his hut," said Squire.

"I'll make some money on them," said Daniel. "They're the kinds the traders want."

"That's true enough," said Israel.

"The next time I'm going to stay two or three weeks. Then I'll get enough skins to take to Philadelphia."

"Daniel," said his mother, "I do not wish thee to make thy living that way. I want thee to be a weaver and live in a settlement."

"I've tried to weave but I can't do it well enough. Father said so. Besides, I can't breathe shut up in a weaving-house."

"Thy father and thy sisters breathe."

The Boones laughed. Then Uncle John said, "Why don't you farm, Daniel?"

"No, no!" cried Daniel. "I don't like farming."

"He feels all shut up in a field," said Sam with a wink at his uncle.

"He can't breathe out on the farm," teased Jonathan.

"I can't," said Daniel gravely. "I've made up my mind. I'm going to hunt and trap for a living. I'll make twice as much as I could weaving or farming."

"And besides, you love it," said Uncle John.

"Yes, Uncle John, I do."

"Well, Dan'l," said his father, "you know more about that than anything else, so I guess that's what you'd better do."

"Squire! How can thee give thy consent!" exclaimed Mrs. Boone.

"I know what you'd like, Sarah," said Squire, "but there's no use trying to shut Daniel up in a settlement."

"He couldn't breathe!" cried Israel, Samuel and Jonathan.

Daniel didn't care how much his brothers teased him. He'd show them what he could do. They'd all be proud of him some day.

3. At the Head of His Class

"Dannie," said his uncle the next day, "your mother has asked me to give you some lessons. Suppose we have a little spelling right now. There is no one here but us."

"I'm not very good in spelling, Uncle John. I didn't get very far in the speller."

"Never mind. I'll soon have you spelling every word in it. Now then, spell bucket."

"B-u-k-i-t," spelled Daniel.

"Wrong. Try again."

"B-u-k-i-t-t."

"No! No! Now listen to me. I didn't say buck*it*. I said buck*et*."

"Oh yes! B-u-k-a-t-e."

"No! No! Not buck*ate*. It's buck*et*—buck*et*. Now then, spell it."

"B-u-k-e-t-t."

"I'm trying to keep my patience, Daniel. But I don't know—I fear I shall lose it."

An hour later Squire Boone and his daughters came home to dinner. They entered the cabin. They stopped at the door. They couldn't get any farther.

Mr. John Boone was taking up the whole room. He was walking back and forth, from the fireplace to the door. His fair complexion was now a bright red. His red hair was redder. His gray eyes looked red, too.

"I can't do it!" he was shouting. "My patience is gone! I'm tired out!"

Then he noticed the others and stopped. He pointed a long finger at the sad-looking boy on the stool.

"He can't spell anything!" he shouted. "He can't even learn, or he will not learn. I don't know which it is."

"I know a third way," said Daniel's father. "He doesn't have to learn."

"He can't spell anything!" Uncle John shouted. "He can't even learn, or he will not learn."

"Squire!" exclaimed Mrs. Boone. "Surely thee does not mean that!"

"Do you want him to grow up ignorant?" asked the angry teacher.

"He won't," said Squire. "He isn't ignorant now. He's the best educated boy in Pennsylvania."

"Not in spelling!" said teacher John.

"He's not going to live in some safe little settlement," said Squire. "He's going to be out in the woods with wildcats, wolves and bears. He's learning ways to protect his life. And spelling isn't one of them."

"But—but——" began John. Squire paid no attention; he went right on talking.

"Daniel has to know the things that count out here in the wilderness. He knows them too. He's at the head of his class. He can read better than any boy in this country."

"He couldn't read for me. At least, I don't call it reading."

"That's because you can't read his books. They're too hard for you, brother. Many a college professor couldn't read them. Listen to the names of them. Tracking. Sounds. Signs. Calls. Directions. Winds. Clouds. Hiding. Throwing. Aiming. Sighting. Shooting. Range. Plants. Poisons. Medicine. Indians. Animals and a dozen others. And Daniel knows them all by heart."

"That's all very well, Squire," said his brother, "but still Daniel should learn to spell."

"No!" said Squire firmly. "Let the girls do the spelling. Daniel will do the hunting. He's ready now to make his own living."

"I give up," said John. "Maybe you are right, Squire."

"Thee is right, Squire," said Sarah. "Dan'l, I'll never worry thee again with lessons."

How that boy loved his family! He could have hugged every one of them, even his uncle.

He stood up, tall and slender. His blue eyes were shining with joy and love and pride.

"Don't blame Uncle John," he said gravely. "He doesn't know any better."

Everyone laughed, Uncle John the hardest of all. And it was a merry, happy family that sat down to the split-slab table a little later.

The happiest and merriest of all was the young Dan'l they were all so proud of—Dan'l who was so highly educated—Dan'l who stood at the head of his class.

XIII

SALT FOR THE SETTLEMENT

1. Bound for the Salt Springs

TWELVE men walked quickly along a forest trail. They were bound for the salt springs near the mountains. Each man led a pack horse. At the head of the long line walked one of the best guides in Pennsylvania, young Daniel Boone.

He was fifteen years old now and he was tall and slender. But he was strong and he could stand hardships as well as these older men. He was used to hardships. He had hunted alone since he was thirteen.

He had spent two winters in the woods, and he knew every foot of the trails clear back to the mountains. He had even lived in that dangerous country; dangerous because a savage tribe lived just over the mountains.

These men bound for the salt springs were all hunters and woodsmen but they had never been in that country. They didn't like to go there now but they had to have salt. Their farm animals were suffering from the lack of it. Soon they and their families would suffer. New settlers had been bringing salt but that supply was about gone.

Daniel was the only one who knew where these salt springs were. He had seen them. But that wasn't the only reason they had asked him to guide them.

They all knew he was "smart about Injuns." He could tell when they were about and he knew how to keep away from them. Hadn't he come back from his hunt every spring with great bundles of furs? Wasn't that proof that he knew how to live in the wilderness?

The men were pleased with their young guide. He was never lost; he never led them into the wrong trails. And he was pleasant with everyone. Nothing excited him or made him angry.

The pack horses were loaded with large iron kettles, skin bags for salt, blankets and clothing. Each man carried a bag of food to eat on the way—parched corn and dried meat.

There was no time to stop for hunting game and cooking it. The sooner they got to the springs the sooner they'd get away.

"I don't believe you could get lost in the wilderness, Daniel," said Jim Pierce one day as they rested.

"Things show me the way, Jim."

"What things?"

"Oh, everything."

And Jim had to be satisfied with that, for Daniel said no more. He never talked much in the woods.

All went well and the party reached the salt springs safely. Camp was made. Fires were started. Great kettles were hung over them. Then these kettles were filled with salt water from the springs and the boiling-down began.

Men with loaded guns guarded those who worked. They took turns at this and also guarding the camp at night.

Finally, after three weeks, their salt bags were filled. Tomorrow they would load the horses and start back. They had had wonderful luck. Not an Indian had been seen and everyone was happy this last night.

At last there was silence. Everyone was asleep but Daniel who was on guard. Suddenly he heard a sound near by. Then he saw an Indian coming toward him. He lifted his gun to fire, but the Indian raised his hands and came closer. It was the Medicine Man!

"S-sh!" the Indian whispered. "Go—leave

camp—quick! Mountain tribe come—at dawn —come. Go—go!"

Before Daniel could speak, the Indian had faded into the night.

Daniel hurried to the men, woke them and helped them load the salt. In ten minutes the long line was ready to start.

2. Covering Tracks

Daniel led them down the bank and into the creek. The water wasn't deep and the salt was in skin bags. It couldn't get wet.

For an hour or so they walked up the creek bed with their heavily loaded horses. Not a word was spoken. Only the splashing of water was heard.

Then they began to talk softly and the same thought was in every man's mind. "Could the Indians track them? Would they pursue them?"

"Even if they do we've got the start of them by a whole night," said Mr. Cross.

"They can't track through running water," said Mr. Miller.

"But there will be tracks from the camp down to the creek," said Mr. Dixon.

"I'm going back and cover those tracks," said Daniel. "I thought I'd start you——"

"Oh no, you won't!" cried Jim. "It's too dangerous. You're coming with us if I have to tie you to your horse."

"Aye!" cried the other men.

"I guess I'll have to, you seem so determined," said Daniel.

"I'm walking right behind you," said Jim, "and I'm keeping my eye on you."

It was a clear night and the stars shone brightly. Daniel pointed to a certain large and bright star. "That's the North Star. I always follow that at night," he said to Jim.

It was at least two hours before he led them back to the trail. At midnight they stopped to rest and water the horses. The men ate a little parched corn.

"Time to move!" said Daniel. The line was formed as before but the guide had disappeared.

"I was afraid of that," said Jim. "He's gone back to save us. They'll get him sure as anything."

"Maybe not," said Ezra Polk. "He's mighty smart at hiding."

"Well, guess I'll have to take charge," said Jim. "He pointed out the North Star to me and he did it on purpose. I can see that now."

Then the long line of men and horses moved on toward the north.

3. Can Daniel Escape?

Daniel went back quickly. "If I can only get there first!" he kept saying to himself. There was no other thought in his mind. He didn't think of his own danger. At least he didn't worry about it.

"I'll outwit them some way," he thought. "I always have."

He reached the camping place just a little before dawn. There were no Indians about as yet.

He worked swiftly. He smoothed the tracks and covered them with leaves. He had now only a few tracks left where they entered the water. Now he had covered them! The savages wouldn't know which way to go. His party was safe!

He had reached the top of the bank when he heard the Indians coming. They were yelling on every side. They had surrounded the camp.

Suddenly it became lighter and they saw him. They yelled with joy and rushed at him.

There was no use to run; they were every-

He swung out over the heads of the Indians on the shore.

169

where. The shore was black with them. He couldn't hide; their eyes were on him. They meant to capture him. That's the reason they hadn't fired.

Then, all of a sudden, he thought of a way to outwit them. He had noticed a large grapevine hanging from a tree close by.

In one instant he had seized it, climbed it and was swinging out on it. He swung out over the heads of the Indians on the shore—out over the creek to the bank on the other side.

Then he dropped to the ground and ran into brush. The Indians shot at him but he was soon out of their range.

At noon he found his party and led them back to Exeter.

Everyone in the settlement praised Daniel.

"You could lead an army through the wilderness, Daniel," said Henry's father.

"Yes, and over the mountains and into the land beyond," said Jim Pierce.

"I'd like to see that land," said Daniel. "I've always wondered what it looked like. Maybe I can figure out a way to get there sometime."

XIV
AT THE GOVERNOR'S PALACE

1. Daniel Warns Surveyors

GOVERNOR DUNMORE sat at the large round table in his library. This was a handsome room on the second floor of the Governor's Palace in Williamsburg, Virginia.

A wide and beautiful stairway led to the library and upper hall from the great hall below. Both halls and library had lovely polished floors.

Across the front of this room were four large windows. From them the Governor could see the street that led to the palace, the high wrought-iron gates to the palace yard and the soldiers who were on guard there.

But His Excellency wasn't looking out the windows this day. He was busy with serious matters. He had sent for his counselors and they now sat at the round table with him.

Some of them were very rich men, the big landowners of Virginia. Others were army officers and owned no land. But rich or poor, they all faced a terrible danger—an Indian war.

"Gentlemen," said the Governor, "I have had very bad news. The Indians are rising up against us. They are determined to drive white men out of this country. Many tribes have united—even those that were bitter enemies. So now thousands of Indian warriors are on the warpath. They have already begun their attacks."

"On the frontier?" asked Mr. Randolph.

"Yes. They have burned cabins and killed many settlers. A fleet of their canoes now blocks the Ohio River. No white man would dare to cross it."

"That is bad, very bad," said Mr. Peyton. "I

believe Your Excellency had sent surveyors to measure land along the Ohio."

"Yes, they went some two weeks ago. There were six of them. So many new settlers wanted to buy that land, it was necessary to have it surveyed. But I had no idea there would be an Indian war at that time."

"None of us had," said Mr. Ball. "The surveyors won't be expecting it, either. They'll be surprised and killed while they're at work."

"I'm trying to prevent that, Mr. Ball. I have sent a scout to warn them. He will bring them back if they will come. But now I fear for his life. The news is so much worse."

"Who is this scout?" asked Mr. Travers.

"His name is Boone, Daniel Boone."

"I have heard of him many times," said Mr. Fitzhugh. "He is said to have great courage."

"They tell wonderful tales about his bravery," said Mr. Travers. "I don't believe them myself."

"Nor I," said Mr. Randolph. "He jumps over cliffs to escape. He kills five Indians who have surrounded him—*five*, mind you."

The landowners laughed, but the army officers didn't even smile. Neither did Governor Dunmore.

"Both stories are true," said Captain Russell. "I have Boone's word for it. That's enough for me."

"The Captain says this scout is honest in all his dealings," said the Governor.

"I worked with him in that last Indian war," said the Captain. "We were both scouts, and I can tell you that there never was a better one than Daniel Boone. He knows the forest as well as you gentlemen know the road to Williamsburg. He is also a master of woodcraft."

"How old is he?" asked Mr. Ball.

"Around forty. And he's strong as a bear and brave as a lion," answered the Captain.

"We can use such a man in our army," said the Governor. "We shall have to send our troops to the frontier to protect the settlers."

"Aye!" cried the others.

"He would be very helpful to us," said Captain Russell. "He could advise our officers when and where to attack. No one knows the Indians better."

"I've heard he knows all their tricks," said a lieutenant.

"And he has a few of his own," said the Captain. "I've seen him crawl up to an Indian village, take a good look from behind a rock and then tell us all about it."

"What good did that do?" asked Mr. Randolph.

"What good!" exclaimed the Captain. "Why, we'd know then whether our force was strong enough to take the town. He'd tell us whether the warriors were there or away, how many families lived there and whether they had enough to eat."

"Hungry Indians don't put up much of a fight," said the Lieutenant.

"But how could he tell so much just by looking?" asked Mr. Travers.

"By the number of fires burning and by the amount of cooking being done."

"Well then," said Mr. Randolph, "the man is wonderful."

"You should see him follow a trail," continued the Captain. "He'd study moccasin prints for a while. Then he would tell us what tribe had passed—the number in the party—how fast they were traveling and how long it had been since they went by."

"Wonderful!" exclaimed the others.

"I am most anxious to meet this man," said the Governor. "Captain Russell, since you persuaded him to go for the surveyors you may persuade him to come here."

"I shall try, Your Excellency."

"I'm afraid you'd be disappointed, Governor Dunmore," said Mr. Travers. "No doubt he's a good scout, but he's a backwoodsman."

"Aye!" said the landowners.

"And they're all alike," continued Mr. Travers, "rude and ignorant."

"He may be," said the Governor, "but I am interested only in his return and in this report about our surveyors.

"Gentlemen, we must now plan for war against the Indians."

2. Daniel—Scout, Patriot, Captain, Counselor

The next day and the next and the next, the Governor of Virginia talked with his counselors. They talked about the army they must send to the frontier—the food—the guns—ammunition and uniforms.

"The scout, Daniel Boone, has come. He wishes to make his report."

On the morning of the fourth day just after the counselors came, one of the palace clerks entered. "Your Excellency," he said, "the scout,

Daniel Boone, has come. He wishes to make his report."

Before the Governor could answer, Mr. Fitzhugh stood. "I'll go down, Your Excellency. I'll get his report. You won't need to meet him."

"Nor see his mud-spattered clothes," said Mr. Travers.

"Nor his muddy prints on the stairs," said Mr. Peyton.

"Nor hear his long stories. These backwoodsmen never know when to stop talking," said Mr. Randolph.

"Gentlemen," said Governor Dunmore, "I thank you, but I wish to see this man. I wish to thank him for his services to Virginia. He may muddy the whole palace. He may talk as long as he pleases. Remember, he risked his life to make this trip to the Ohio. He was not obliged to go."

The Governor turned to the clerk. "Mr. Paxton, I will see Daniel Boone at once."

"Gentlemen," said Captain Russell, "you need not fear for his manners. He is always quiet and talks very little. In fact, I doubt if he will talk at all, except to answer questions."

Then the door opened and the clerk entered with Daniel Boone.

"Mr. Boone, Your Excellency."

Daniel bowed to the Governor. Then he bowed to the others. After that he stood quietly waiting for the Governor to speak.

Daniel was tall and slender, but powerful. His calm quiet face showed his patience and honesty. His keen blue eyes showed his intelligence.

Every man in the room knew a gentleman stood before them. True he had not stopped to change his deerskin clothing but there was no mud on it. Nor did he leave muddy tracks on the polished floor.

The Governor hastened toward Daniel and

gave him his hand. "I welcome you back, Mr. Boone. I feared for your safety."

"I was able to get to the surveyors in time, sir. I brought them back safely."

"Hooray!" cried the officers.

"Ah!" said the landowners.

"Come," said the Governor. "Please sit here at the table and tell us all about it."

"There is nothing to tell, sir."

"Nothing!" exclaimed the Governor. "You went eight hundred miles through a trackless wilderness. You were surrounded on all sides by savages. The very fact that you are here, alive, proves that you outwitted them."

"I had to do that, sir," said Daniel modestly. "Won't you tell us how you did it?"

"Well, I know just about what Indians will do and I try to keep ahead of them."

"How did you get this knowledge?"

"I've studied them for more than thirty years, Governor. I began when I was a boy in Pennsylvania. I learned their language. I have been a prisoner in a Cherokee village. I've hunted and fished and trapped with them. I've had them for friends. Not one has ever been disloyal to me."

"Why, you surprise me, Mr. Boone," said the Governor. "You seem to think well of them."

"I have never heard Mr. Boone say he hated Indians," said Captain Russell.

"I'm sorry you don't hate them, Mr. Boone," said the Governor. "We are about to send an army against them. I had hoped you would enter it."

"I have never said I would not fight them, Governor, for I would. They must be conquered. They must be driven out of this land."

"Aye!" said the others.

"If we do not conquer them, they will conquer us. America will again become a wilderness. There won't be a farm or a settlement anywhere."

"Aye!" cried the others again.

"The day of the white man will be over. We shall be driven to the sea and then into it."

"Mr. Boone," said the Governor, "will you take charge of a company? You shall have the rank of Captain."

"If I had no rank at all I would go, sir. It is my duty to fight for my country."

"Mr. Boone," said Mr. Randolph, "you are a good patriot. I'm proud that we have such a man as you in this army."

"I'm proud to have such a man in Virginia," said Mr. Ball.

"Aye!" cried the landowners.

"We'll be proud to serve with you, Daniel," said Captain Russell.

"Aye!" cried the other officers.

"And I," said Governor Dunmore, "will be proud to have you sit at my counsel table as one of my counselors."

XV

COLONEL DANIEL BOONE

1. On the Other Side of the Mountains

JUST at noon one day an elderly man rode his horse into the little town of Lexington, Kentucky. His hair was white but he was strong and powerful. He sat erect in the saddle and rode his horse like a young officer.

He stopped when he came to the schoolhouse, and tied his horse to a hitching post. He stood for a moment watching the children as they came out. He smiled and nodded to a group of big boys who came first. Then he went on toward a row of little shops.

"I know him!" cried one of the boys. "It's Daniel Boone!"

"It couldn't be," said another boy. "He doesn't

An elderly man rode his horse into the little town of Lexington, Kentucky.

live here in Kentucky now. He moved away out west."

"He's back on a visit," said the first boy. "My father saw him yesterday and talked with him."

"Oh then, that's who he is!" cried the second boy. "Let's follow him. I want to see him."

"So do I! So do I!" cried the others.

The news spread like fire. Soon a crowd of

boys was following the Colonel. He was their hero. He was the most wonderful man in the world to them. No other had had such adventures in the woods. No one else had escaped so often from savages.

Men saw the boys running and heard the news. Soon a crowd of them was following the boys. Daniel Boone was their hero, too. They knew that a braver man never fought Indians. And they knew he had been made a colonel because of his courage.

They knew, too, that they could thank him for everything they owned in this new land across the mountains.

"There wouldn't be a house or a farm in all Kentucky if it hadn't been for Daniel," said a man.

"No, nor a shop, or church, or schoolhouse," said another. "He brought the first settlers into this land."

"It was a dangerous journey," said a young man. "How did he ever persuade them to go?"

"Because people believed what Dan'l told them," said an old-timer. "When he said he'd been over here hunting, we knew he had. When he said this soil was rich, we knew it was."

"Aye," said an old hunter. "And when he said there were thousands of buffaloes over here, we knew he'd seen them."

"Then there was another reason," said an old trapper. "Dan'l blazed a trail through the mountains and clear to this meadowland before he ever took a woman or a child across."

"But wasn't there danger from those savage Indians?" asked a woman.

"Not very much," answered the trapper. "The most of them had been driven out of the mountains. There were only a few prowling about."

"Well, they could attack settlers," said the woman.

The old trapper shook his head. "Dan'l always knew when they were about."

"There never was such a leader," said an elderly shoemaker. "He took care of the sick just as good as any doctor. He knew what kind of herbs to use for medicine."

"And he was never excited or angry," said an elderly tailor. "No matter what happened he was always calm and patient. I came over with him and I know."

"Aye!" nodded the old-timers.

Just then a boy came running back to the men. "He's gone into the hat shop," he said, "and the door is closed."

"I'll wait," said an old hunter, "if I have to wait all night. He might never get here again."

"Aye!" cried the others.

2. Many States Claim Daniel

"He's buying a hat," said a boy. "I peeped in the window."

"A hat!" exclaimed a girl. "I thought he always wore a coonskin cap."

"Not any more," said a doctor. "He doesn't live in the wilderness now. He lives on a big farm in Missouri."

"Why, that's all wilderness away out there!" exclaimed a cooper.

"It isn't now," said a stranger. "I'm from Missouri myself. There's settlements and towns all the way, and we can thank Daniel Boone for that. He was one of our first settlers. Hundreds followed him and cleared the land and made homes."

"I believe Missouri claims him as one of her sons," said a teacher.

"She does; we're all mighty proud of him out there."

"Pennsylvania claims him, too," said the teacher. "She says he was born there."

"Yes, but he grew up down in North Carolina where I come from," said another stranger. "His folks moved there when he was around sixteen. So we think we've got a pretty good right to claim him."

"Virginia claims him, too," said a tobacco grower. "He had a farm close to mine for a time. He fought with the Virginia troops in that Indian war. He helped to save the Virginia frontier."

"We'd like mighty well to claim him down in Tennessee," said another stranger. "He never actually farmed there, but he did a lot of hunting in our country."

"Seems to me Kentucky has the best claim of all," said the teacher. "He really started this state and he lived here a long time and farmed here."

"Aye!" cried the Kentuckians to a man.

"Why did he move around so much?" asked a boy.

The older men smiled. "I can tell you," said one. "Daniel always felt crowded when too many settlers moved near. He said he couldn't breathe close to towns and settlements."

"Ha, ha!" laughed the crowd.

"He helped to make America a great and strong country," said a preacher. "He, and he alone, opened the door to these rich valleys and plains beyond the mountains. He led the way. Thousands followed him."

"It's the truth!" exclaimed a lawyer. "He knew America couldn't grow as she was—a narrow strip of land between the sea and the mountains."

"I wonder what he thinks now," said a judge. "Cities, towns, villages and farms everywhere."

"I hope he takes pride in it," said the preacher, "for it's all the result of his work."

"Aye," said the others.

The shop door opened and Colonel Boone stood in the doorway. He wore a homemade suit

Daniel smiled and took off his hat and waved it.

of cotton, leather shoes and his new broad-brimmed hat of black felt. He was very neat and trim.

His splendid face showed his intelligence, his honesty and his patience.

"Hooray!" the crowd yelled. "Hooray for Daniel Boone!"

Daniel smiled and took off his hat and waved it.

"Hooray!" they yelled again. "Hooray! Hooray!"

THE END